Look Out the Window

Look Out the Window

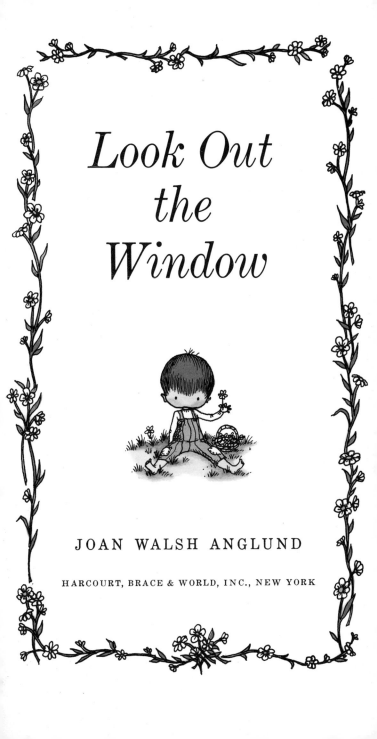

JOAN WALSH ANGLUND

HARCOURT, BRACE & WORLD, INC., NEW YORK

Library of Congress catalog card number: 59-9271
Printed in the United States of America

For

Look out the window....
What do you see?

Houses . . .

lots of houses....

High dark houses
with shades pulled down
and iron fences all around...

or squatty happy houses
with doors and windows open to the sun . . .

or tiny teeny houses with lace curtains
and a neat row of tulips along the path. . . .

But of all the different houses
          in this whole wide world...
there is no other house
          that is quite like *your* house.

Sit on a chair....
Who jumps on your lap
and starts to purr?

Your cat....

You've seen dozens and dozens of cats...

fluffy, soft cats
that sit in the sun
all day . . .

stringy, slinky alley cats
that hide behind garbage cans
and run away when they see you . . .

quiet cats, lapping up milk
with prickly tongues...

jumpy cats, playing
with bright balls of yarn...

angry cats,
arching their backs
and hissing
at a sudden noise...

black cats,
white cats,
striped cats,
spotted cats. ...

But of all the cats in this whole wide world,
there is no other cat
that is quite like *your* cat.

Run out the door....
Who follows you?

Your dog....

Look around. You'll see there are
many, many dogs . . .
dogs with long hair . . .

dogs with short hair . . .
dogs with hardly any hair at all . . .

busy dogs with waggy tails . . .
or old dogs with tired eyes . . .
or frisky dogs with bones to bury . . . .

But there is no dog...
no other dog in this whole wide world
that is quite like *your* dog.

Take a walk down the street....

What do you see?

People...

lots of people...

men and women . . .
short and tall . . .
thin and fat . . .
happy and sad . . .

people walking . . .

people riding . . .

people working . . .

people talking . . . .

But of all the people in this whole wide world...
there are no two people that are quite like
your very own mommie and daddy.

Now, you can look out a window...
sit in a chair...
run out a door...
walk down a street...
ride on a bus...
or go to a school...

and wherever you go,
you'll see
lots and lots of children...

all kinds of children...
little children...

big children...

busy children...

lazy children...

children jumping rope...

children flying kites...

children building forts...

children planting seeds...

or sailing boats...

or selling lemonade . . .

or chasing cats . . .

or *even*
children sitting very still. . . .

But try as you may,
you will never, never, never
find another child
that is quite like you,

because you're the only one
in this whole wide world
that is *you*.